W9-AOW-053

Bruno Munari's

ABC

DEDICATION

He who buys this book

may make the dedication

to the child who receives it

_____

_____

Munari picture books

ANIMALS FOR SALE

THE BIRTHDAY PRESENT

THE ELEPHANT'S WISH

TIC, TAC, AND TOC

WHO'S THERE?
OPEN THE DOOR!

JIMMY HAS LOST HIS CAP

THE WORLD PUBLISHING COMPANY

CLEVELAND AND NEW YORK

E

MIDDLEBOROUGH ELEMENTARY SCHOOL LIBRARY
313 WEST ROAD
BALTIMORE, MARYLAND 21221

79-103

WITHDRAWN

by
Bruno
Munari

Published by
THE WORLD PUBLISHING COMPANY
2231 West 110th Street, Cleveland 2, Ohio

Published simultaneously in Canada by
Nelson, Foster & Scott Ltd.

Library of Congress Catalog Card Number: 60–11461

COHW
Copyright © 1960 by Bruno Munari
All rights reserved. No part of this book may be reproduced
in any form without written permission from the publisher,
except for brief passages included in a review appearing in a
newspaper or magazine. Printed in the United States of America.

A

an Ant

on an Apple

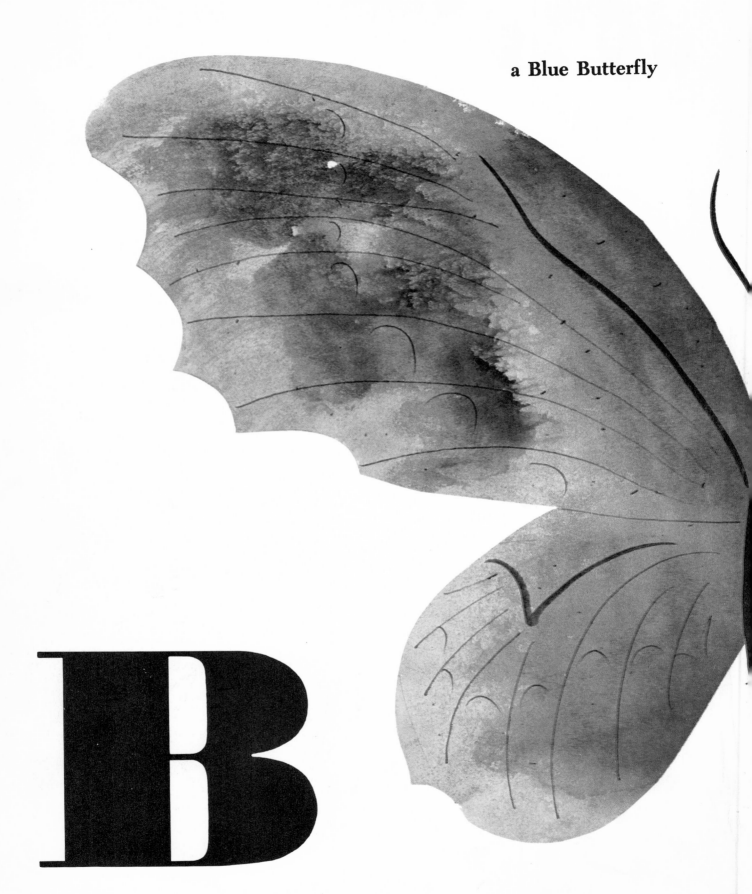

a Blue Butterfly

B

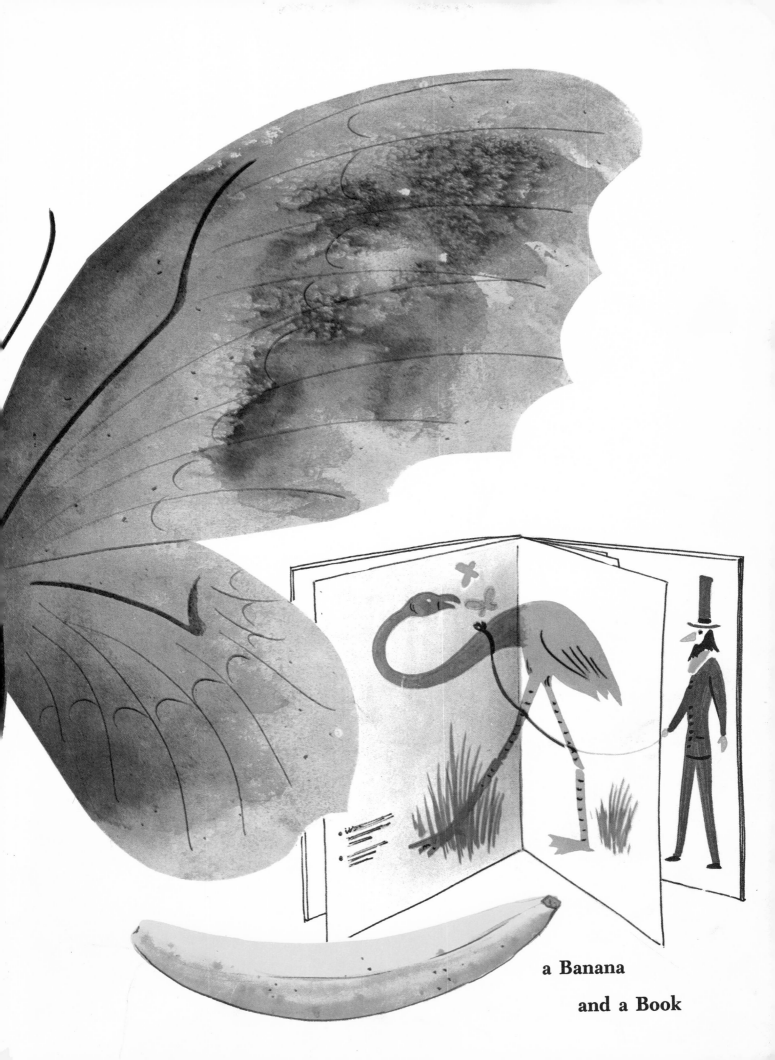

a Banana

and a Book

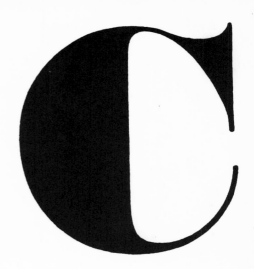

a Crow

on a Cup

a Candle

and a Cat in a Cage

a Drum

a Dog
and his Dish
outside a Door

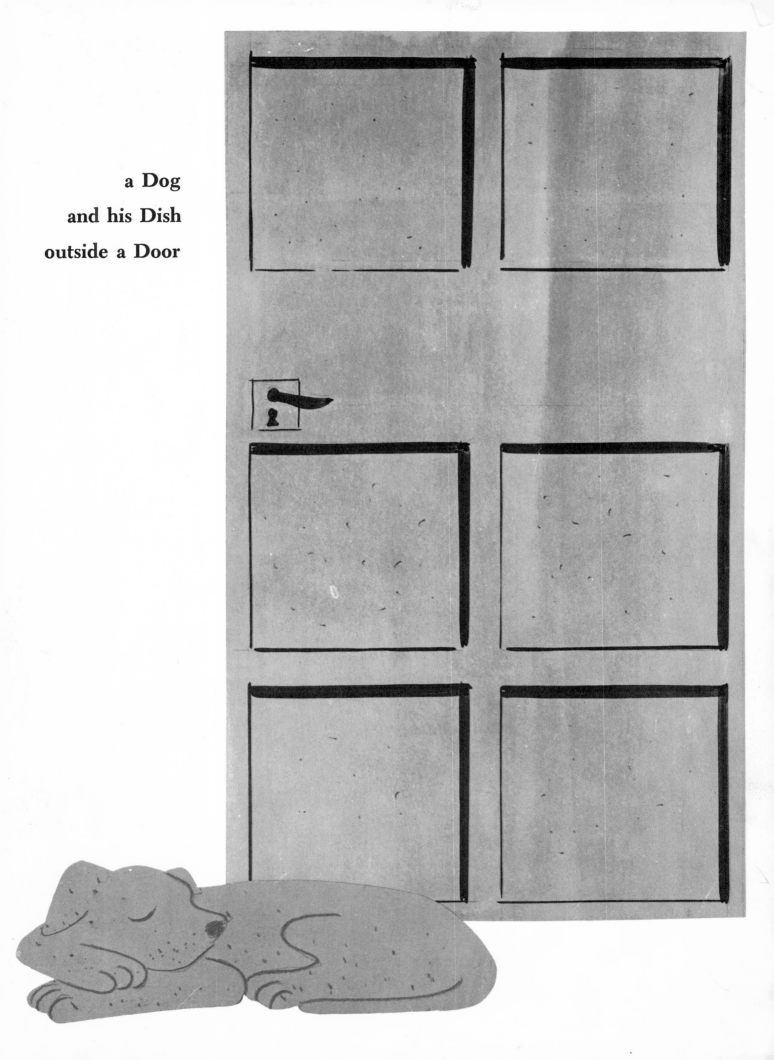

an Elephant

an Egg

an Eye
and an Ear

a Flower

a Fly

F

a Feather

more Flies

and a Fish

Glasses in Green Grass

still another fly!

and a Gift for you

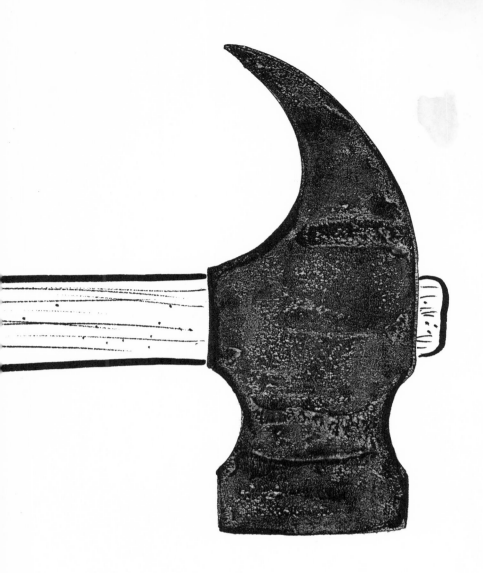

a Hammer
over a Hat

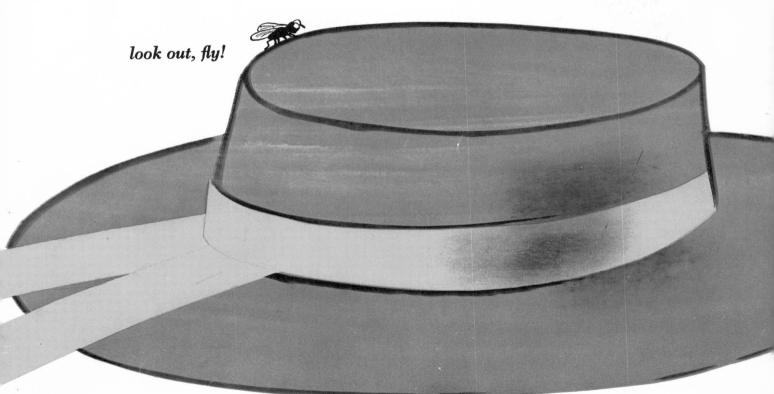

look out, fly!

I

shoo, fly!

lots of

Ice Cream

a Juggler

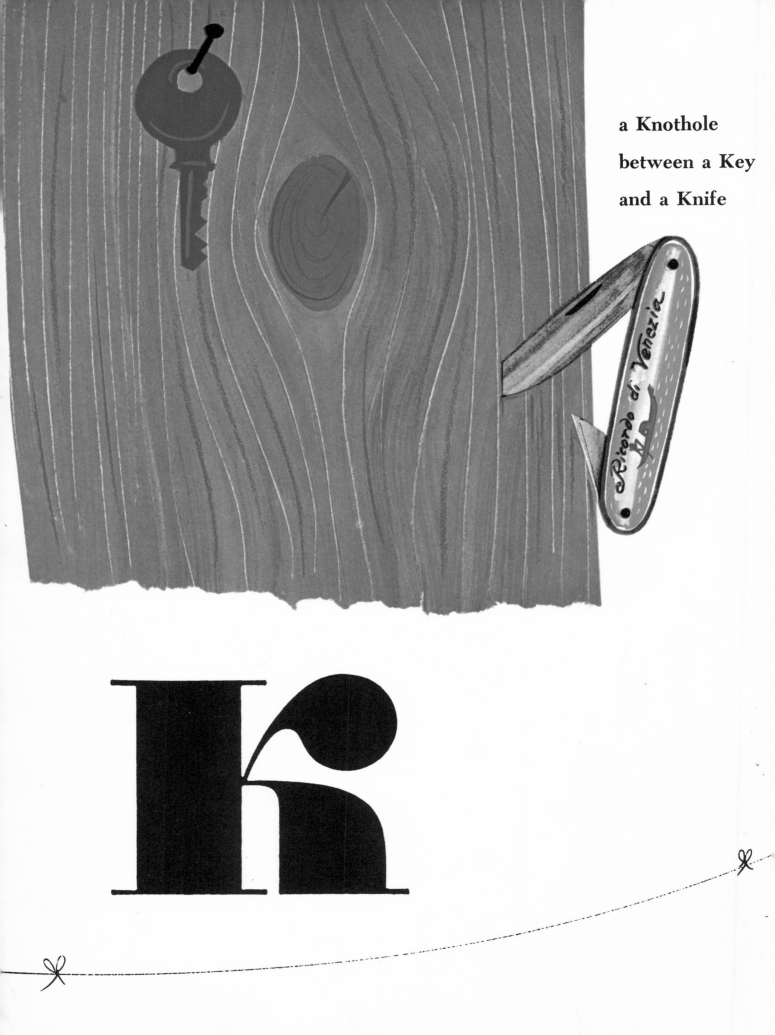

a Knothole
between a Key
and a Knife

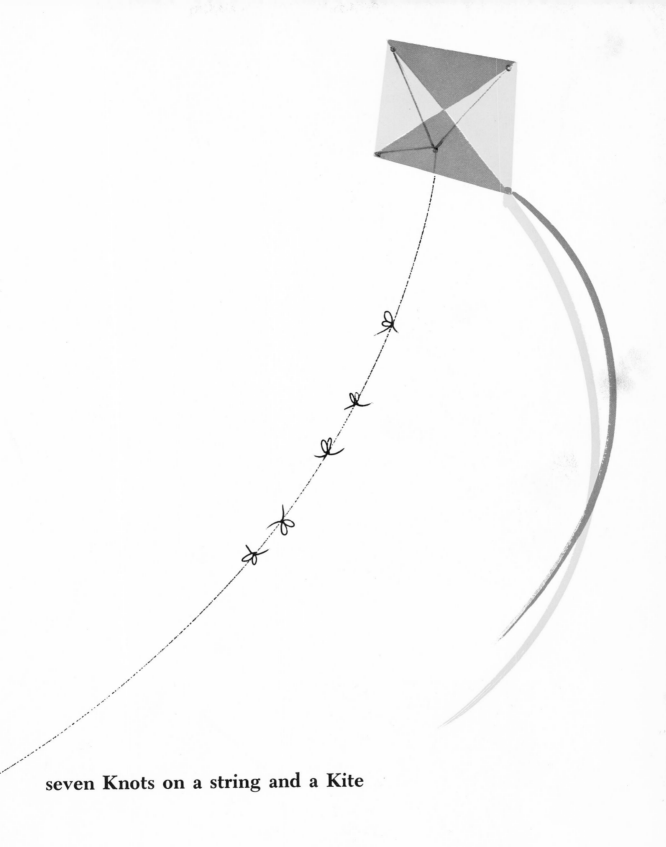

seven Knots on a string and a Kite

a Long Leaf

a Leaf

a Little Leaf

L

and a Lemon

a Match

M

a Monkey

and a Mouse

No bird in the Nest

N

Nuts on a Nail

an Owl

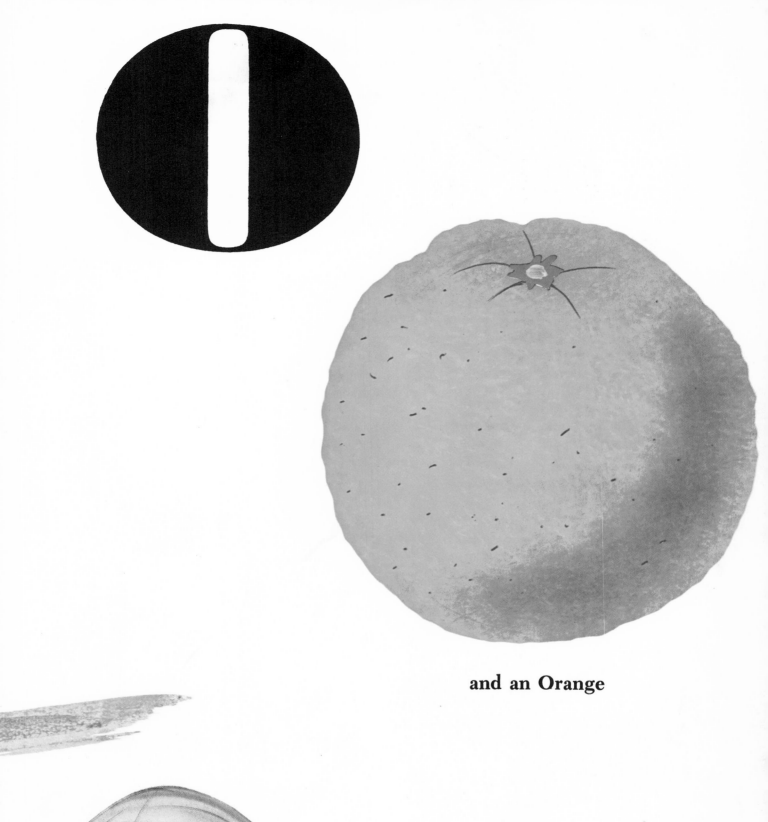

and an Orange

and an Onion

a Piano

a Package

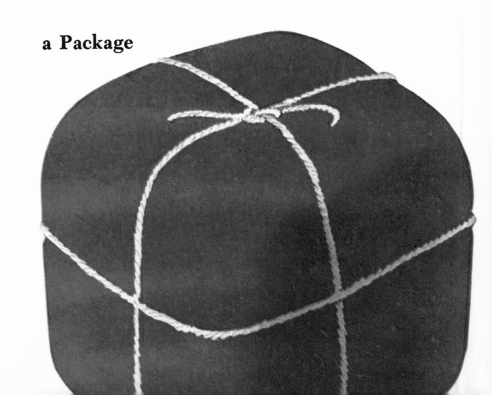

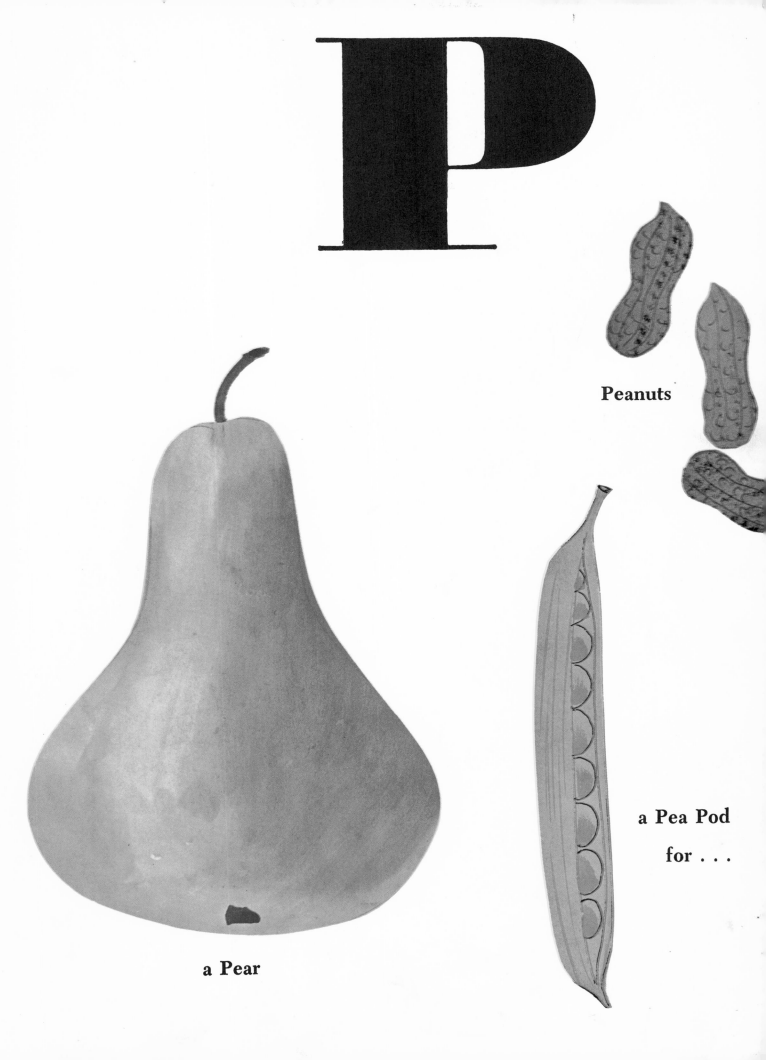

P

Peanuts

a Pear

a Pea Pod
for . . .

a Quail

R

a Rose

and a Red Ribbon

a Sack
of Stars
and Snow
for
Santa Claus

STOP

and a Sign

all kinds of Shells

even a Ship

and a Stone

T

a Trumpet

a Ticket

a Telephone

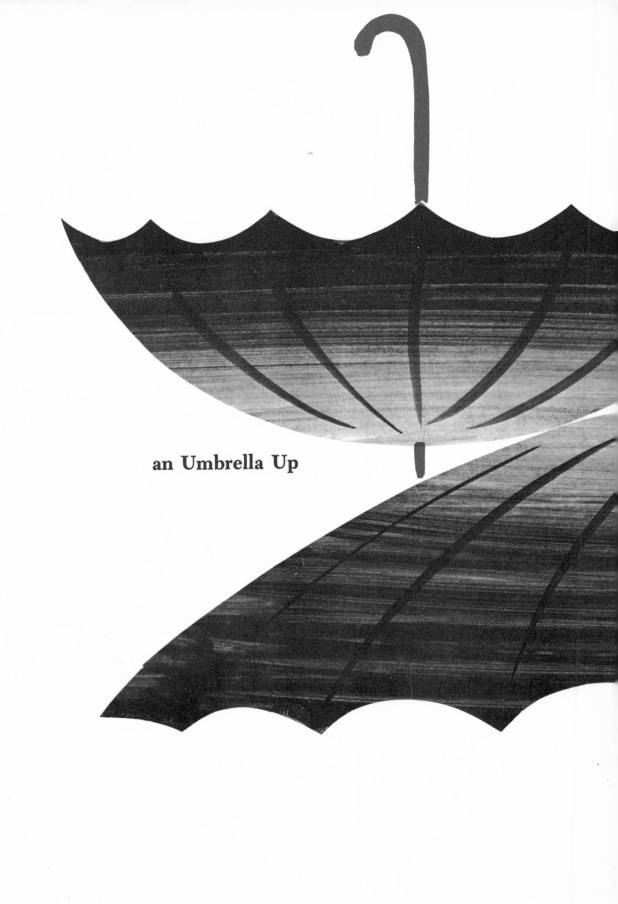

an Umbrella Up

and an Umbrella

Under the Umbrella

a fly on a Voyage

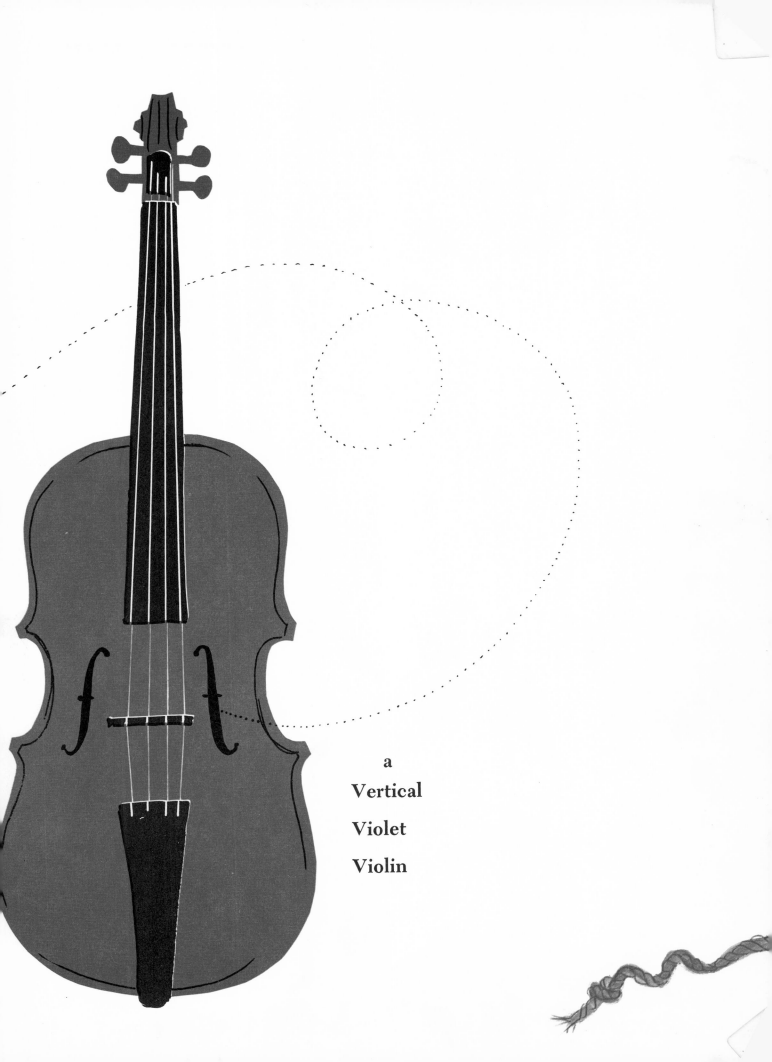

a
Vertical
Violet
Violin

a Watermelon

on a Wagon

with a Wooden Wheel

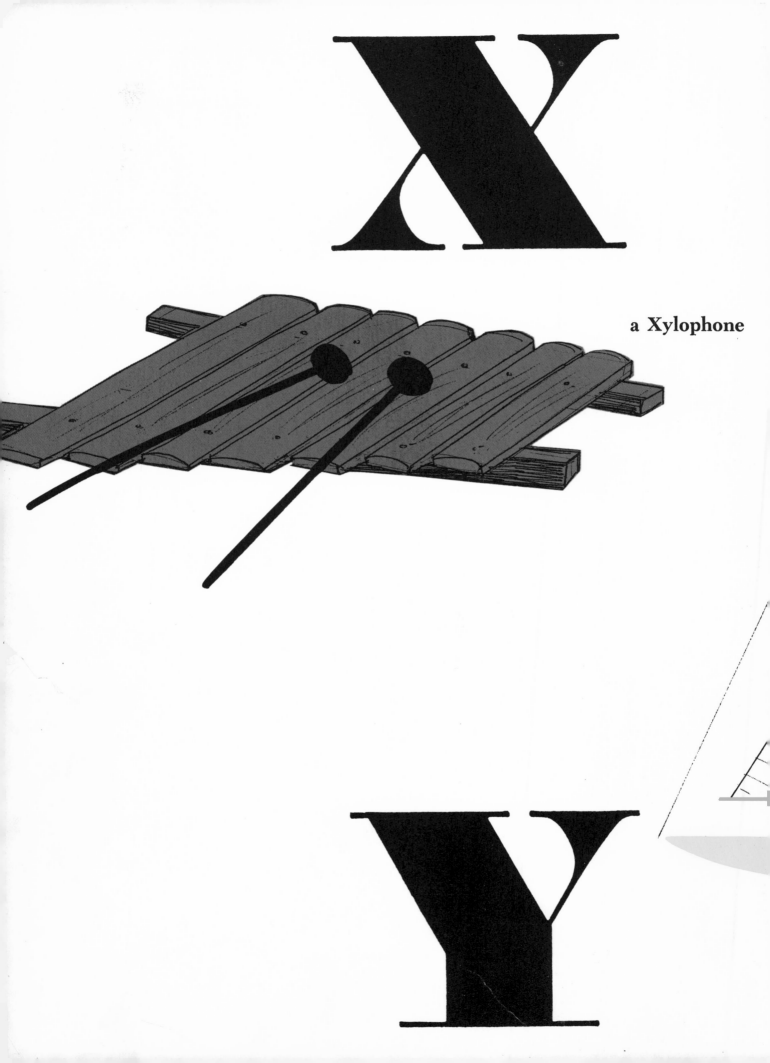

X

a Xylophone

Y

a Yellow Yacht

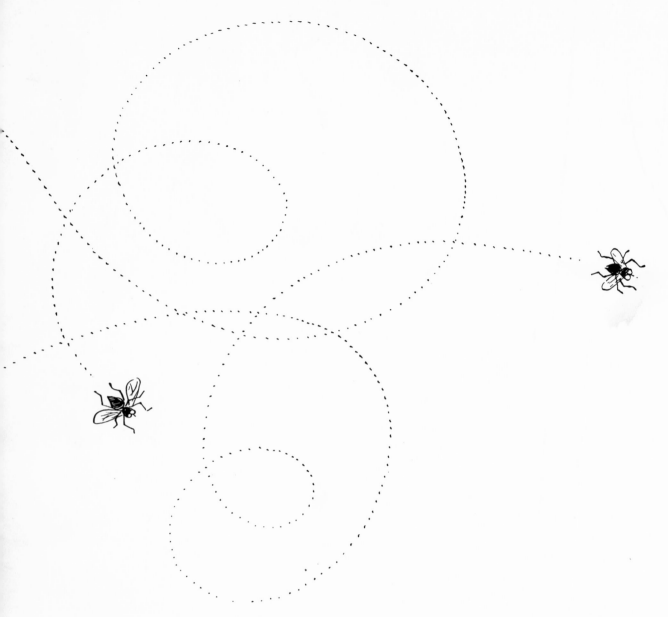

a fly going Zzzz....